Pilled up

Entry level

Acknowledgements

Cover design: Oliver Heath, Rafters Design

Illustrations on pages 5, 7, 9, 11, 13, 15, 17, 19, 25, 27, 29, 31 and 35 © **Paul Gardiner, 2005.** The right of Paul Gardiner to be identified as the illustrator of this work has been asserted by him in accordance with the Copyright, Design and Patents Act, 1988.

Brinsford books are a direct result of the findings of a two-year authoring/research project with young offenders at HMYOI Brinsford, near Wolverhampton. Grateful thanks go to all the young people who participated so enthusiastically in the project and to Judy Jackson and Brian Eccleshall of Dudley College of Technology.

First published in Great Britain by Axis Education Ltd

ISBN 1-903685-96-6

Axis Education PO Box 459
Shrewsbury SY4 4WZ

Email: enquiries@axiseducation.co.uk

www.axiseducation.co.uk

The pill was small. It had a picture of a bird on it. I did not know what to do with it. But there it was. I swigged it down with a slug of WDK and looked at my mates. Paul asked if I could feel it.

I just shook my head. Maybe I had taken a dud. I could not feel much. Paul was dancing like a mad thing.

He must have been off his head. The beat of the music shook the floor.

I nodded my head in time to the beat. I started to sweat. I knew I looked stupid but I felt great.

I felt happy. I mean really happy. I could not stop smiling. It felt like we had been best mates forever.

I kept on dancing and moving fast. Then I began to slow down. I asked Paul for another pill. It cost three quid. It was worth it.

I was buzzing again. I felt brave as a tiger. I knew I could go up to this girl.

"Want a drink?" I asked.

5

She smiled and nodded. I bought her a drink and we stood at the bar. My eyes began to roll in my head. I was having the best time ever.

"We are going back to the flat," Paul told me.
"Want to come?"
"How about you? Want to come too?" I asked the girl.

We stayed up till 5 in the morning. We smoked draw and drank beer. I must have fallen asleep. When I woke up they had all gone.

I looked round. The room was a blur. I tried to swallow. My mouth felt as dry as a desert and just as gritty. My lips were cracked. I needed water but I felt really weak. The clock said 3 pm. Where had the time gone?

Where was Paul? Where was the girl?

I went back to the sofa. Last night was a real buzz. I wanted to do it again. And I could see a way to make some cash.

I had to call Paul. I called his mobile.

"You alright?" asked Paul.

"Great."

"You were crashed out when I left."

"Yeah, yeah. Listen. Can you get me some more pills?"

"How many?"

"50," I said.

"Wow! That many?"

"Yes. On sub. I will sell them easy."

That evening Paul gave me a small plastic bag. It did not look much for £150.

I got myself ready. I was still feeling weak. But I would wait till I got to the club.

I was early. It was only 9.30. But I needed to pop a pill.

Suddenly I felt 100% better.

Life was great. I was selling pills on Tuesday, Thursday, Friday and Saturday nights. I loved it.

I had loads of money. People knew me. I was the man.

I told Mum and Dad I was stopping with a mate.

I saw the glass collector look at me. Did he see me pass the pill to that kid? Nah. Even if he did, it didn't matter. I was the man. I was safe.

I saw the first bouncer coming towards me. Dancers got out of his way. My heart started hammering. Oh shit.

I started to back up – right into the second bouncer. They walked me into a room without saying a word. "Turn out your pockets. We think you are selling pills."

15

"Nah, man. Look." I emptied my pockets. Put my fags, money, gum and stuff on the table. They would never find my stash. I was safe. They checked everything. "Sorry, mate. Looks like we made a mistake."

I thought I'd got them. Then he looked at me. "Be warned, if you are selling drugs in this club you will not be able to walk for a while."

I tried to look as if it was nothing to do with me. "Yeah, well. I'm not doing nothing so it don't matter."

I felt the tiny bag move down my leg. Oh shit. The pills were stashed down my jeans and they had worked loose. My guts began to move up and down. I needed the toilet. The little bag dropped out of my jeans leg.

The biggest bouncer pushed me against the wall. "Undo your jeans."

What the hell?

He saw my face and slapped me. "I'm going to search you. That's all, you stupid bastard."

I undid my jeans. I tried to think how many pills I had left. Could I make them believe they were for my own use?

The police took me to the station. My Mum came.

"I can't believe you got mixed up with drugs, after all the stuff on telly about it. How many times have I told you about pills?"

She went on and on at me.

I did not get sent down. I just had to check in to the police every month for a year.

I was buzzing. Find a new club and start again.
This time I got my mate Steve to hold my cash for me. I chatted up the bouncers and gave them the odd pill to keep them sweet. We moved to this new club. There was a group selling pills for £7 each. We sold ours for a fiver and soon took over all the deals. We even had the bouncers on our side.

200 pills on a Friday, 150 on a Saturday. I was making £900 on a weekend. I bought an Astra SDI. It was red. Steve and I shared it. I spent the money on beer and girls and gifts for people. I bought loads of coke and crack. Life was a buzz.

One night in the club a skinny kid came up to me. "Sell us a couple of pills."

The club was banging. I had sold about 150 pills. "Meet you in the gents."

As I walked through the door I knew something was not right, but it was too late.

Three lads jumped me. They started to search me. At first I did not care. My stash was in a jock strap. I would be OK anyway. The bouncers were my back-up. They would be in soon to sort it out.

The manager walked in. "What's going on?"

"He's selling drugs, mate. His type is scum. He should not be let in a decent club."

"Search him properly. We need to find his stuff."

They soon found the pills and my money in the jock strap. No one was holding my cash that night.

"These yours?" The manager counted the pills and money. "Christ! There are 51 pills and 165 quid here. Call the police."

"Look, mate." I was sweating. If I ended up in court I'd get sent down this time for sure.

"Cut me some slack," I said. "I have not been selling in your club. I promise I will never come back here again. You can flush the pills and keep the money. I will just go and you will never see me again."

"If I call the police I will have even less to worry about," said the manager. "You will not be selling that crap to anyone. The streets will be a bit safer – for a while anyway."

He called the police.

"Do you want us to phone your Mum, son?" The policeman looked old enough to be my Grandad.

"Nah. I am safe. It is all a mistake. They were not mine. Honest, guv. They was planted on me by those guys at the club."

"Why would they do that, son?"

"I am not your son."

Browning J H
DOB: 18/04/1987
Date: 12/12/04 22FA

2004/22FA/39/893987G

I was still pilled up. I could not sit still. I kept getting up and walking round the room. I sat down, then got up again.

I walked about bit more. Sat down. Stood up.

"We will keep you safe in a cell for a bit," said the policeman. "Looks like you need calming down a bit."

They banged the door and bolted it. I was sure they shut it hard so it would sound worse. I could not sit still. I was so pilled up.

I could not believe they had charged me. All the time thoughts were rushing round my head. I had so much energy that I was doing push-ups.

The police gave me bail. I had been in the cells three hours. What could I do? I did not want to go to jail. My Mum came to get me. She must have seen how down I felt. She did not shout or nag me. She just looked really sad. She took me for a meal. Then we went home.

The big day. I lay on my bed smoking a spliff. I could not believe I might get sent down. I could not believe I might not be back in my room for ages. I was up for the Crown Court. I was told I could get four and a half years. I hoped I would get less because of my age.

Waiting for the Crown Court case had given me more time. I smiled to myself. I had not sat on my bum all that time. Ever since the police bail I'd become a one-man crime spree. I had still been selling the pills, but on the street because I was too well known in the clubs.

I had been nicking cars as well. I did not mean to at first, but someone had left their keys in. What else do you do? It was a good way of getting a bit more cash. The cops had no idea it was me doing it.

"John Henry Browning, you are charged with ..." My guts turned over. I could not hear the rest of the charge. I thought for one horrible moment I was going to be sick.

"How do you plead, guilty or not guilty?"

"Not guilty, Sir."

I looked at the jury. What would they decide?

The trial was set for five days but by the second day I could see the way it was going. I changed my plea to guilty.

On the third day the judge gave me 18 months. I gave a sigh of relief. It was a lot less than I thought. I would be out in nine months. I looked across at my Mum. She was crying. Her son was a jailbird now.

I hoped to God they did not find out about the cars. At least I had got away with them for now. My legs shook as the guards took me down the stairs to my new life in prison.

Glossary

draw   cannabis

judge   the person in charge of a crown court case who decides how criminals should be punished

police   the organisation that protects against crime and enforces the law

spliff   a cannabis cigarette